# This Book Belongs to:

_____

This book is dedicated to my grandparents
(Ted, Katy, LeRoy, and Nancy),
my parents (Tony and Dawn), and my wife
and sons (Kelsey, Sawyer and Finn).
From tree to seed to seed to tree,
you are the inspiration for this book.

# TREE OF LIFE .....

## by Mitch Rady

illustrated by Jeff Fay

SJ and Finn were smart and
curious little guys.
With everything they saw,
it was whos,
whats, wheres, and whys.

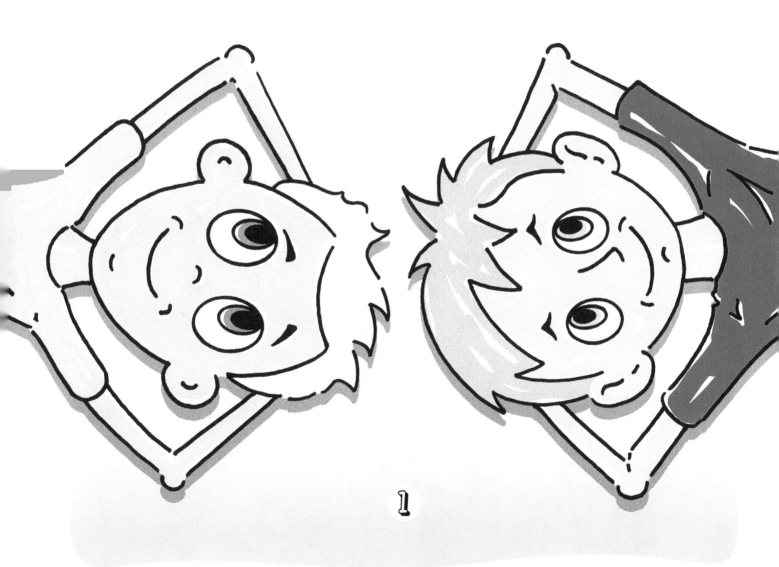

Dad said "
Let's take a walk outside.
There are many lessons
to learn from the earth
and the sky".

2

Come my sons,
let's go for a walk and see.
I want to show you
my favorite tree.

You see, you see
this beautiful tree. It has a lot
in common with you and me.

The leaves of this tree blow free in the wind.
The roots grow grounded, deep within.

The leaves will fall and grow back,
year after year. As the trunk grows
little by little, it will persevere.

The branches take twist and turns
in search of the sun. The roots reach for water
deep underground.

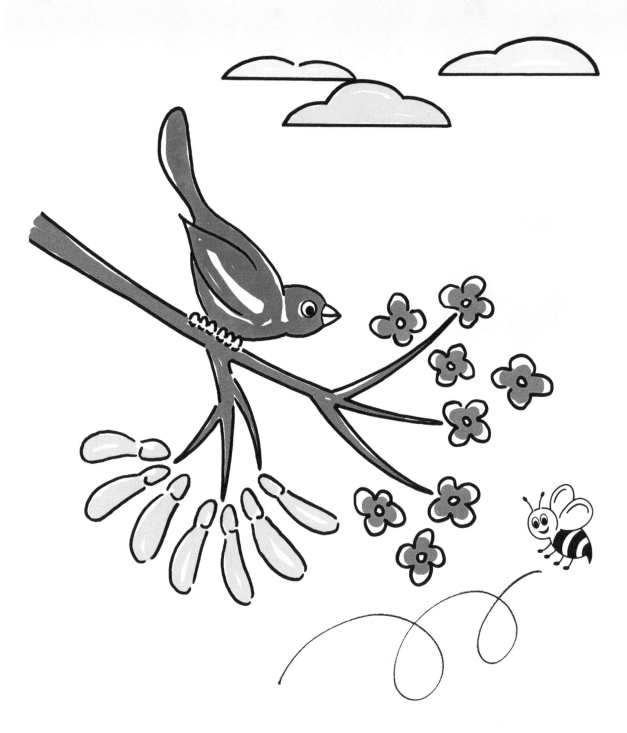

As this tree takes in, all of its
growing needs. In return, it gives gifts
to the birds and the bees.

So different can be, the roots
from the leaves. Yet both
grew from the same small seed.

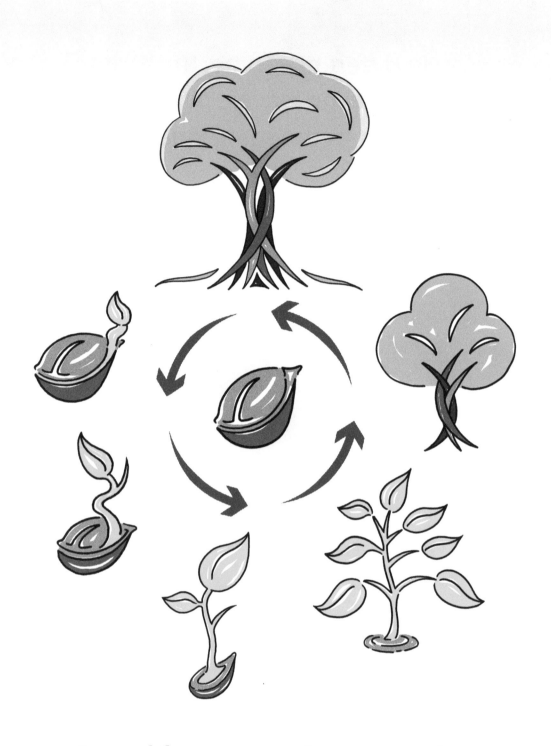

A seed from a tree, from a seed
from a tree doing whatever it needs
to see the next succeed.

You see these questions we ask,
can be answered by the world around us.
If we take time to listen and learn,
You will find its love that surrounds us.

Life's meaning may be unknown,
but its purpose is this. Leave this world
a better place, for the next to exist.

12

9 780578 853758